This book is a special gift for:

With much love and respect from:

I Respect You, I Respect Me

ELIZABETH A. GARCIA-JANIS MD

Illustrated By: Sudipta (Steve) Dasgupta

Introduction

This book has been especially written for all children, and their parents, grandparents, guardians and all those loving people who helped raise our youth. This children's book for all ages encompasses many ways that we interpret what respect means in various cultures. It helps us understand that RESPECT comes in many different forms.

The virtue of respect allows us to be more loving to one another. It allows us to interact with our Creator, others, and nature in a kind and gentle manner. Learning the meaning of respect at a young age allows us to grow up valuing others and ourselves. It adds to a sense of well-being and an ability to get along with others in our world. It leads to a general sense of inner peace and joy knowing that we are a part of each other and our beautiful world. Respecting others and ourselves is the beginning of understanding the interconnectedness of people and nature to the universe and our Creator. It allows us to know the significance of others and our own self-worth and this can only lead us to a life of meaning and purpose. May respecting others and yourselves bring you a more peaceful and beautiful life.

With love and respect,
Elizabeth A. Garcia-Janis MD

✳✳Dedication✳✳

This book is lovingly dedicated to my children, Alex and Jackie. You are both the love of my heart.

This is also for all the children of the world and their parents, grandparents, relatives and friends who help raise them.

May the basic virtue of RESPECT anchor you and honor you in your incredible journey throughout your very precious lives.

I respect you, I respect me

Once, there was beautiful little town surrounded by majestic snow-capped mountains reaching up to a multi-colored sky.

1

In that town, each morning, the flowers always blooming, the grass stays greener than green, and the birds sing around a magical waterfall where the doves fly by.

The mountains had the colors of lavender and purple when seen as the sun gently rises.

The little town was studded with pine trees, with many animals of all kinds, happily scurrying around with their own special surprises.

5

One bright sunny day, a sweet and curious girl named Amanda,
came back from school along with her happy and active brother named Sterling.

On their way home, they were both distracted by the squirrels and bunnies,
the butterflies and the lady bugs, but most of all by the birds of different colors,
joyfully singing.

Amanda and Sterling were learning about many interesting things in school
and today their teacher challenged them to find out more about RESPECT.

The teacher told them that RESPECT was a good thing to know for our growth
and our character; it was an important subject.

Close to their home, they saw their mother reading a book under a tall sturdy tree. They ran towards her and sat beside her looking so inquisitively.

With a puzzled look on her face, Amanda asked her mother,"Mom, what is RESPECT? Our teacher wants us to know more about it."
Her brother Sterling also excitedly wanted to know and it made it hard for him to just calm down and sit.

Their mother looked at their questioning faces, and with her loving and gentle eyes, she said, " RESPECT is many things, my dears.
Respect is something that no one fears.
It is something that we don't expect.
It helps us inside to choose to respect."

Love & Respect Cafe
Love & Respect Cafe
YOU ARE IMPORTANT
Thank You Very Much

RESPECT is what we choose to do, to give value to others and you.
It is a gift to others and ourselves, so we know that our hearts are true.

Respect is something that we give to others, with gentleness that is wanted.
When we say "Please" and "Thank you", then respect is being granted.

When we speak with others with kind words each day,
when we listen with attention to what others say,
we can also show respect that way.

When we greet others, especially our elders, and we appreciate their wisdom,
they respect us back in such a way that we feel inside a lovely calm.

When we give our attention to our elders, and we learn from all they tell us,
our minds become more peaceful and our hearts feel nice and warm.

In respecting our elders, we put their hand on our forehead for a blessing, gently.
and in turn, it gives us joy when they give us a smile back, so affectionately.

12

Sterling said, "When we follow good direction from teachers, and help with chores at home, we give respect that way.
We can choose to practice these good deeds, each and every day."

Amanda added, "When we ask others as to how they are, and we care as to how they are doing,
we are paying RESPECT to the life they have, even when we are coming and going."

Their mother looked at her children lovingly and said, " Why, I think you're both getting the idea about RESPECT.
What you are both saying , I'm glad to say, is totally correct."

When we give a kind regard for what others are feeling, we give RESPECT in that way too.

When we write a letter to apologize, or say we are sorry, if we accidentally hurt other's feelings, respecting others makes us not feel so blue.

Sharing with others is a form of respect, and we are thankful for the love that we get.
Giving each other some healthy space is also a way to RESPECT a friend, so let's not fret.

We also need to respect ourselves with our time to think and meditate and pray.
These allow us to respect ourselves, before we even begin to play.

Giving ourselves some quiet time, is to be respectful of ourselves, when we get
frustrated with the things that happen.
Instead of fighting with others or being too angry, we take our own time-out to
let our tensions fly, way out into the open.

When we sit together in silence, and respect us not wanting to talk,
and we just feel each other's presence and be there for another, just like a rock.

Respect is about being in awe of the amazing sunrises, and we thank our
Creator for painting the sky.
What a beautiful morning surprise we see as we take it all in and gently sigh!

When we dance with sheer joy and want others to be happy,
we RESPECT ourselves and others, instead of being crabby.

Respect is when animals are cared for and we appreciate the plants, the trees, the flowers, the rain showers and more.
We respect how they help us, feed us, and are there for us to soothe our core.

Respect is whispering to a horse about our lives and our woes.
We know the horse will listen and give us comfort, give us peace if we have foes.

23

Respect is loving and protecting our wonderful, beautiful Earth.

RESPECT is God's love, though we may not know it, He knows all our worth.

When we do to others what we like done for ourselves,
RESPECT is what is behind this wise thought.
If we think in this manner, and we practice RESPECT,
perhaps no war will ever be fought.

When we choose to give RESPECT to others,
we will likely get respect back as well.
When we pray to God and we pray for others,
we'll respect ourselves, no worries to quell.

So, Amanda and Sterling, my dears, my loves, so sweet,
now you know about RESPECT, so we have to get off our feet.

As we play and learn all day and our health we are to keep,
we RESPECT our bodies and ourselves by making time for sleep.

I respect you, You respect me. It's all a beautiful part of Love.
I respect you, I respect me. RESPECT is a gift from GOD above.

I respect you, I love you. I respect me, I love me.
Respectful, loving people, we hope and pray we all can be.

Sweet dreams, happy dreams as we go on and slumber
Sweet dreams, happy dreams, RESPECT, may we all remember.

****See you again tomorrow,
Good night, with love, for now
My kiss will take away your sorrow
With deepest love and respect,
.... I bow.****

32

About the Author:

Elizabeth A. Garcia-Janis MD DFAPA is a double board certified Child and Adult psychiatrist who has dedicated her life serving those who suffered disasters, losses and tragedies. She served as Chief Medical Officer and Medical Director in various psychiatric organizations and hospitals.

Dr. Garcia-Janis volunteered doing intensive short term disaster relief work in many parts of the world: the Mt. Pinatubo volcanic eruption in the Philippines, the Katrina evacuees in Houston, Texas; the tsunami in Thailand; the Nicaraguan refugees in Costa Rica; and uplifted Clean Water for the World in Uganda. She also responded to the tribal emergency declared by a Lakota Native American tribal president to help with suicide prevention among the youth.

Dr. Garcia-Janis was granted the Distinguished Fellow award by the American Psychiatric Association. She was also awarded Physician of the Year in 2009 by the Medi-Star Medical News. The Leading Physicians of the World organization honored her as Top Psychiatrist in 2013. She has received numerous recognitions regarding her humanitarian work locally and globally.

For many years, Dr. Garcia-Janis has treated many children and adults with mental health problems like depression, anxiety, bipolarity, ADHD, PTSD, Schizophrenia. She has been an unwavering advocate in the empowerment of children and adults who struggle with their mental health. De-stigmatization of mental illness, uplifting the beauty of diversity, and educating people about the healing power of Nature and profound spirituality, have been at the forefront of her personal missions. Dr. Garcia-Janis values the unquestionable significance of Love and Respect as vital to the health and well-being of human beings.

She founded the Phoenix Global Humanitarian Foundation and its mission is to serve those who suffered disasters, losses and tragedies.

Dr. Garcia- Janis authored the following books:

The Courage to Encourage,
The Phoenix Miracle,
An Island Woman's Heart,
Your Compassionate Nature
Utmost (co-authored with Dr. Ashis Brahma),
The Princess Who Loved All (children's book for all ages)
✺✺✺✺✺✺✺✺✺✺✺✺✺✺✺✺✺✺✺✺✺✺✺✺✺✺

❊ Acknowledgment ❊

I would like to acknowledge Sudipta "Steve" Dasgupta for all his hard work on the illustrations of this book. He spent several months working with me, discussing the feelings behind the lines when necessary, and doing countless revisions to bring each page to life.

My profound gratitude to Sudipta "Steve" for his consummate artistry, creative vision, putting to life the concept of respect and his ongoing collaboration to create this beautifully-illustrated book.

About the Illustrator:

Sudipta Dasgupta, also known as Steve, began drawing with chalk on the floor when he was around 3 years old. Later, he joined a local art school near Kolkata City, India. After his school finals, he enrolled in the science stream to pursue higher education. He soon realized he wanted something different than the stereotypical schooling system, and took on the challenge of getting accepted into a good art college. In the year 2006, he graduated from the Government College of Art & Craft at the University of Calcutta.

Initially, Sudipta spent many years practicing painting on canvas with different mediums. Then in 2009, he began to get offers to work on storybook illustrations from many companies and individual authors. Since then, he has been a full-time book illustrator and has worked with nearly two hundred companies and individual clients worldwide. Aside from book illustration, he also enjoys craft, painting, graphic design, murals, as well as many other forms of art. For more information about Sudipta Steve Dasgupta, please visit :
www.dasguptarts.com

❄ Endorsement ❄

"Encased in a seemingly simple plot, this story profoundly captures the depth of the meaning of Respect.

Tucked in its pages are seeds of wisdom - that one can grow through the practice of respecting one's self and others...

A practice that can lead to a doorway that opens our understanding and the experience of the divine. That which is in us. In all of us. And is all that is."

"Beautiful."

Julie Ann Arellano MD
Mother
Wife
Psychiatrist
Creative Soul

Questions To Ponder With Our Little Ones:

1. What have you learned about RESPECT?

2. What are ways that you can show RESPECT towards others?

3. Who are the people you think are respectful?

4. When did you show RESPECT to others?

5. Did anyone give you RESPECT today?

6. Did you show others RESPECT today?

7. How do you RESPECT Nature?

8. How do you feel when you are respected?

9. How can you show respect to your parents?

10. How can you show respect to your grandparents?

11. How can you show respect to your teachers?

12. How do you show respect to your friends?

13. Do you think respect is a part of loving others?

14. How do you show respect to animals?

15. How do you show respect to plants and trees?

I Respect You, I Respect Me

Paperback ISBN: 978-1-63812-163-3
Hardcover ISBN: 978-1-63812-165-7
Ebook ISBN: 978-1-63812-164-0

Published by Green Sage Agency   12/14/2021

Green Sage Agency
1-888-366-9989
inquiry@greensageagency.com

CPSIA information can be obtained
at www.ICGtesting.com
Printed in the USA
BVHW021107110222
628491BV00023B/540

9 781638 121657